THE PERSONALITY POTION

ALAN MACDONALD

Illustrated by John Eastwood

Oxford University Press

Oxford University Press, Walton Street, Oxford OX2 6DP

Oxford New York
Athens Auckland Bangkok Bogota Bombay
Buenos Aires Calcutta Cape Town Dar es Salaam
Delhi Florence Hong Kong Istanbul Karachi
Kuala Lumpur Madras Madrid Melbourne
Mexico City Nairobi Paris Singapore
Taipei Tokyo Toronto

and associated companies in
Berlin Ibadan

Oxford is a trade mark of Oxford University Press

First published 1996
Reprinted 1997

ISBN 0 19 916913 6 School edition
ISBN 0 19 918516 6 Bookshop edition

Printed in Great Britain by Ebenezer Baylis

Illustrations by John Eastwood

Kit Kane, Kid Detective

Danny Doolan was doing what he liked best. He was curled up in his bed reading.

He had a chocolate fudge bar he'd been saving all day. (Fudge bars were his favourite.) The bedroom light was off. He was using a torch under the covers to read his new library book. It was called *Kit Kane, Kid Detective*.

Kit was on the trail of the gangster, Slugs Malloy. Slugs had kidnapped Kit's girl, Susie, and taken her to a meat factory. He was about to put her in the mincing machine.

Unless Kit got there soon it would be too late. Susie would be served up as meatballs.

Suddenly the door burst open...

'Danny, what do you think you're doing under there?'

It was Danny's mum. She switched on the light.

Danny stuck his head out. He blinked like a mole coming out of its hole.

'Nothing. Just reading.'

'But it's only six thirty. It's nowhere near your bedtime.'

'I know. I just want to finish my book.'

'Why don't you go out? Call for one of your friends.'

'I don't want to. I'm busy.'

'Why don't you go over to the park? Go and play football or something.'

'Oh Mum! I'd rather stay here and read.'

His mum gave him one of her looks. The look that meant you're not normal. His parents were always saying stuff like this.

'Why don't you behave normally?' Or, 'It's not normal for a boy of your age.'

Danny couldn't help it. He didn't want to go and play football in the park. He preferred to watch telly or read his book. Especially if the book was as good as the *Kit Kane* detective series.

His mum tried one last time. 'You can't spend your life hiding in your bedroom, you know.'

'Why not?'

'It's not ... normal.' She sighed heavily and shut the door.

Danny got up and turned off the light. In the dark, he pretended he was Kit Kane sneaking into the factory to save Susie. He crawled on his hands and knees towards the bed.

'Okay Slugs, this is the end of the line!' he drawled in an American accent.

He dived on his pillow and wrestled it to the floor. In the fight that followed, his fudge bar got a bit squashed – but it was all in the line of duty.

The empty seat

The next day started badly. The bus to school was crowded. His best friend, Sparrow, waved to him but the seat next to him was taken. The only spare seat was next to Duncan Wicks.

Wicks was in the year above and Danny always kept out of his way. He'd seen Wicks pick on younger kids in the playground. He made them hand over their sweets or drinks.

If they argued, Wicks gave them a wrist burn. He gripped their wrist hard and twisted his hand until they cried out. Danny bet it really hurt.

Danny pretended he hadn't seen the empty seat. But Wicks had seen him.

'There's a seat here, Specs. I'm not going to eat you.'

Danny sat down. He hated being called Specs.

Wicks didn't move along, so Danny had to perch on the edge of the seat.

Wicks pointed to Danny's bag. 'Got your lunch in there?'

'No,' Danny lied. 'I have school dinners.'

Wicks nodded. He pretended to be looking out of the window. Then he made a grab for Danny's bag.

Danny held on, but Wicks punched him on the arm. Danny bit his lip to stop himself crying out.

'Let's have a look then,' said Wicks, unzipping the bag.

He took out Danny's lunch box and said in a dumb voice, 'Well I never – sandwiches! Your mum must have forgot you have school dinners.'

Everyone on the bus was looking over now. Danny saw Laura Mills watching. Laura was in his year. With her springy black hair and dark eyes she was just the kind of girl Kit Kane would have as his girlfriend.

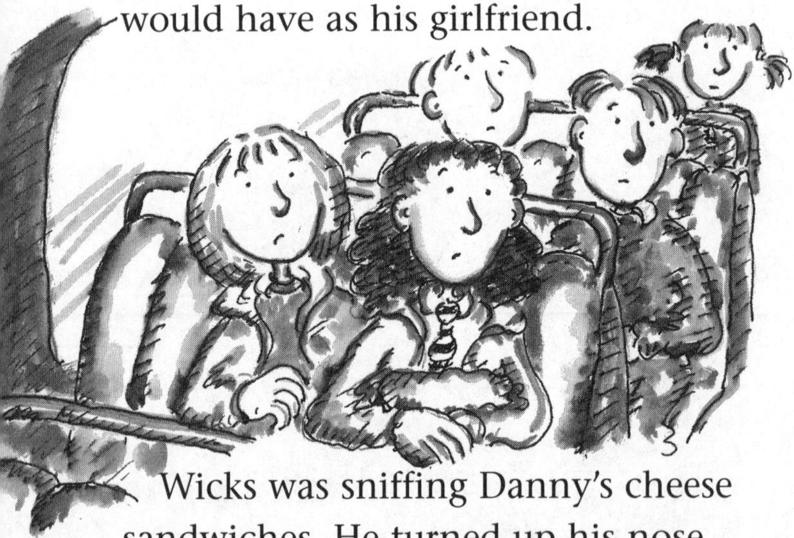

Wicks was sniffing Danny's cheese sandwiches. He turned up his nose and went to put them back. Then he spotted the fudge bar at the bottom of the box.

'This'll do. Thanks, Specs,' he said, pulling off the wrapper.

'That's mine! Give it back,' said Danny hopelessly.

Wicks grinned and took a big bite. 'Mmm, not bad, Specs. You can bring me another of these tomorrow.'

Danny turned away.

In his imagination, he pictured what would happen next if he was Kit Kane.

Kit stood up and pulled Wicks out of his seat by his jacket.

'Why doncha pick on someone your own size, dogsbreath?' he drawled.

'D-d-don't hurt me,' stammered Wicks.

Kit swung Wicks round his head three times and let go. Wicks flew through the air and landed in the lap of a surprised old lady who bashed him with her umbrella. The whole bus cheered.

But that only happened in Danny's imagination. In reality, Danny sat there staring out of the window.

He knew his face had gone red. He felt stupid and helpless.

Sparrow ran after him as they went into school. He was the smallest boy in the class and always seemed to be running to keep up.

'Hi, Danno. I saw what Wicks did to you on the bus,' he chirped.

'Yeah.'

'He's just a big bag of beef.'

'Yeah.'

'I bet if anyone had the guts to stand up to him, he'd cry like a baby.'

Danny stopped suddenly. 'I didn't see you being so tough.'

Sparrow looked surprised. 'What could I do? I was only saying ...'

'Yeah well, don't say – unless you're going to do something. That's the trouble round here. No one ever does anything.'

Sparrow went away to hang his coat up. He looked hurt. Danny didn't know why he'd said that. He just felt angry inside. Angry with Wicks. Angry with himself for looking stupid in front of everyone else.

Danny's teacher, Mrs Morgan, had some news for them. Anyone who wanted a main part in the school play could come to the audition next Monday.

Danny didn't usually take any interest in the school play. Once, in his first year, he'd been a sheep in the Christmas play. All he had to do was go 'Baa!' and lie down to sleep.

But this year the play was called *Bugsy Malone*. It had music and songs and, best of all, it was about gangsters. Danny listened spellbound as Mrs Morgan told them the story.

He began to imagine himself in the part of Bugsy. He'd borrow his Dad's old suit and wear a hat pulled down over one eye. He'd chew gum and talk in his Kit Kane accent.

By the time Mrs Morgan had finished talking, Danny knew he'd be perfect for the part of Bugsy.

It was a great idea. But it wouldn't work. Mainly because he knew he hadn't the nerve to try for the part. The thought of standing up in front of everyone made him feel sick inside.

The potion

On the way home from school, Danny stopped at Uncle Hal's. Uncle Hal was an inventor. This meant spending hours out in his garage making a noise. The only trouble with Uncle Hal's inventions was that they never got finished. He always said they still needed 'a little fine tuning'.

Then he forgot all about them and started on something else. Danny had liked the self-sucking straw which made milk bubble by itself.

The underwater chess set had been another good idea. But Uncle Hal couldn't remember where he'd put it. His garage was crammed to the ceiling with old pipes, tubes, boxes, bottles, and funny-smelling powders. He spent most of his time looking for things among the chaos.

Danny banged three times on the garage door. It lifted up and there was Uncle Hal wearing a pair of purple glasses. The glasses had two small light bulbs on the top of the frames. Uncle Hal touched a button behind his ear. The glasses lit up.

'Clever eh? What do you think?' he asked.

'They're amazing,' said Danny. 'What are they for?'

'Seeing in the dark.' Uncle Hal shut the garage door behind them. He turned off the lamp on his work bench.

'Now, imagine there's a power cut and you haven't got a torch. You switch on your Light Specs and – hey presto! – you can see.'

'Can I try them?' asked Danny, taking off his own glasses.

Danny switched on the Light Specs.

'All I can see are two blobs of light. They hurt your eyes,' he said, disappointed.

'I know,' said Uncle Hal. 'They still need a bit of fine tuning.'

He switched the lamp back on and started to take his invention to pieces.

'So, how was school today?'

'It stank,' said Danny.

'Usual stink or anything special?'

'There's this kid called Wicks. He picked on me on the bus today. He's about ten times the size of me. He punched me and stole my fudge bar.'

'A big time crook, eh?'

'Yeah. And you know what I did? With the whole bus watching? I sat there and did nothing, like a dummy.'

'Very sensible, I'd say. Never take on a bully ten times your size for the sake of a fudge bar. After all, when did a fudge bar ever fight for you?'

Danny shrugged. 'That wasn't the worst thing. They're going to do this play at school. It's called *Bugsy Malone* and it's about gangsters.'

Uncle Hal raised one eyebrow. 'So what's so bad about this play?'

'Nothing, it's great. I'd like to be in it. I really want to be Bugsy. But I can't.'

'Why not?'

'I won't be able to do the audition. I'll be so nervous I'll stammer like an idiot. No one's going to pick someone like me to play Bugsy Malone.'

Uncle Hal put down the Light Specs and looked at Danny.

'So you don't think you can get the part?'

Danny nodded miserably.

'Well, come and see me on Sunday. It'll take some work, but I might be able to help.'

Uncle Hal wouldn't say any more. He just tapped his nose and said, 'Sunday.'

Danny thought about it all week. What could Uncle Hal do to help him get the part of Bugsy Malone?

Early on Sunday morning he rang Uncle Hal's doorbell. Uncle Hal showed Danny into the garage.

'Ready?' he asked. Danny nodded. He hadn't any idea what was going to happen.

Uncle Hal fetched two test tubes. In one was an inky green liquid, in the other some white powder.

He measured a little from each carefully into a bottle.

'What is it?' whispered Danny.

'Something I've been working on all week. I call it my Personality Potion.'

'Personality Potion?' Danny's eyes widened. 'What's that?'

'It brings out the hidden talents that no one knows are inside you. You'll see.'

Uncle Hal mixed the potion in the bottle. It frothed and fizzed.

He held it up to the lamp. The potion seemed to glow in the light as if it was full of stars. Danny took the bottle and looked at it in wonder.

'You mean this can help me get the part in the play?'

'You'll be brilliant.'

'But how do you know it really works?'

'See for yourself. Try it tomorrow,' said Uncle Hal.

He opened the garage door. Danny went out into the bright morning light, holding the Personality Potion tight in his hand.

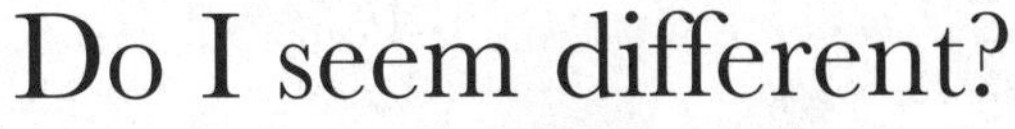

Do I seem different?

Waking up on Monday morning, Danny thought the potion must have been a dream. But there it was on his bedside table, where he'd left it the night before.

He took off the lid and sniffed it. Then he took a small sip. The taste was sweet and bitter at the same time. Danny drank some more and let it slip down his throat.

Jumping out of bed, he ran to look in the bathroom mirror.

There was no doubt something had happened to him. His head didn't droop and his eyes were brighter than usual. He didn't even feel worried about the day ahead at school.

Danny sat next to Sparrow on the bus. He could see Duncan Wicks on the back seat. He hoped that Wicks had forgotten about the fudge bar. Danny had one in his bag but he didn't want to hand it over.

Sparrow was chatting away about a space film he'd seen on TV, but Danny found it hard to listen. He was wondering whether he looked different to other people. The Personality Potion was in his pocket – just in case he needed it again.

He looked over at Laura Mills. Could she see any change in him?

'Do I seem different to you?' he asked Sparrow suddenly.

Sparrow blinked at him. 'I was telling you about the bit with the aliens.'

'I know, I just wondered if I seem any different.'

Sparrow examined him. 'No. You've got green skin and three heads just as usual.'

At break, Danny and Sparrow talked about the school play. Sparrow said Mark Shaw would probably play Bugsy. Mark was captain of the football team and he got chosen for everything. Danny said he might even try for the part himself.

Sparrow gaped at him. 'You? You play Bugsy Malone?'

Before Danny could answer, he saw Wicks. He was on the far side of the playground and he was coming straight towards them.

Danny didn't have any time to think. Quickly, he fumbled for the Personality Potion and took a drink. If it really worked he desperately needed it now.

A group of girls stood between Wicks and Danny. Wicks barged his way right through the middle, knocking one of them over. Danny just had time to notice it was Laura Mills before Wicks was on them.

'Specs! I've been looking for you.'

'Oh have you? What for?'

'Where's my fudge bar? I told you to bring it today.'

'He must have forgot,' Sparrow said bravely.

'Who asked you, midget?' said Wicks, raising his fist. Sparrow ducked away.

Wicks held out his hand to Danny. 'Fudge bar, Specs. You'd better have it.'

'It's in my bag,' said Danny, '...but there's one problem.'

'Oh yeah, what?'

'You can't have it.'

He was amazed at the words he'd just spoken. It must have been the potion speaking. Wicks' mouth was open but nothing was coming out.

'Say that again,' he said at last.

'I said it's my fudge bar. You can get lost.'

A crowd was gathering round them. Danny could see Laura and her friends at the front. No one had ever told Wicks to get lost before, and they wanted to see what would happen.

Danny felt scared but also reckless. It was as if the potion had released a cork inside him.

Wicks took hold of Danny's arm and started to twist.

'You go and get it right now, Specs.'

'Sorry, no. I think you should lay off the sweets, Wicks. Your teeth are going green.'

'What did you say?'

'They're green. Everyone calls you Grotgums.'

The crowd laughed. They couldn't believe their ears. Here was quiet Danny Doolan, standing up to the worst bully in the school.

Wicks was furious. He started to twist Danny's arm harder. Danny felt as if it was on fire.

Then he heard Laura Mills' voice call out, 'Let him go, Grotgums!' Someone else took it up and soon the whole crowd was chanting:

'Grotgums! Grotgums! '

Wicks stared round at them, his face as red as ketchup. He liked to pick on younger kids when they were alone. He wasn't used to facing a whole crowd shouting at him.

The noise had reached a teacher who was heading that way.

Wicks let go of Danny's arm and ran off.

Danny watched him go. It was incredible. He had stood up to Wicks and survived. The potion really worked. It changed him into a different person, someone who could do or say anything.

People were staring at him in a new way. One of them was Laura.

'Thanks for starting that,' he said to her.

Laura smiled. 'Serves him right for pushing me. Is your arm okay?'

Danny had forgotten his arm. 'Yeah,' he said, bravely. 'It just stings a bit.'

'What got into you?' asked Laura. 'He could have murdered you.'

'I was sick of him. I had to do something.'

At this point the bell went. 'Well, see you later,' said Laura. 'Are you going to the audition this afternoon?'

'Yes ... yes, I am,' said Danny hastily. 'In fact I'm going to try for the part of Bugsy.'

He walked away feeling two metres tall. He had spoken to Laura Mills. After a whole year, he'd finally spoken to her. And she hadn't laughed at him, she'd talked back. Then he remembered – he'd said he was going to the audition.

Even worse, he'd said he was going for the main part. The part of Bugsy. How could his mouth have landed him in so much trouble?

The big scene

Danny sat on one of the chairs in the hall, waiting for his turn to audition. A lot of people had come to watch. They filled four rows of chairs. Laura Mills sat with her friend, Yasmin. Mark Shaw was there with his usual gang.

Danny sat on his own. Sparrow hadn't come. He said he couldn't bear to see Danny make an idiot of himself.

Danny was next but one to read. He fingered the potion nervously. The bottle felt hot and sticky. As long as he could drink it just before reading, everything would be okay.

The last person before Danny was Wicks. He thought he was just the person to play a gangster. Mrs Morgan gave him a page of *Bugsy* to read. But Wicks was the world's worst actor.

He read the lines as if it was the weather report. There were a few sniggers from the back rows. Wicks looked up furiously.

'That'll do Duncan, thank you,' said Mrs Morgan. 'Daniel Doolan, you're next.'

Danny took a deep breath and stood up. He heard Mark Shaw whisper to his friends, 'Doolan? This should be really funny.'

Danny unscrewed the lid of the potion and got up to walk to the front. As he got to the end of the row, he lifted the bottle to take a drink. But Wicks, on his way back to his seat, barged into him on purpose.

'Oh, sorry, Specs, didn't see you there!'

The bottle spun out of Danny's hand and smashed in pieces on the floor.

Danny looked down in horror at the green puddle by his feet.

'Come on, Daniel, you'll have to clear that up later,' called Mrs Morgan, crossly.

He stood in front of everyone while she told him off for bringing drinks into school. Then she pointed to the page. 'Now start there and read to the bottom.'

Danny tried to think about the words. But they seemed to swim around like tadpoles on the page. Without the Personality Potion, he knew he couldn't do it. He couldn't even speak. His throat was dry and his face was burning up.

He made a sound like a car engine trying to start.

'Ehurrh!'

Looking up, he could see Mark Shaw and his mates in fits of giggles.

'Speak up Specs, can't hear you!' jeered Wicks from the back of the hall.

Danny's gaze shifted to Laura Mills. She was glaring at Wicks. Then she looked straight at him and nodded. 'GO ON!' she mouthed.

Danny was amazed. Why should she care that he was making an idiot of himself? He shut his eyes. He tried to think how Kit Kane would have read the part. Then he took a deep breath and started to read.

After a while he realized that the giggling from the back rows had stopped. The hall had gone quiet. Everyone was listening. And he was doing it! He was saying the lines in the American accent he'd practised hundreds of times under his bedcovers.

The longer he went on, the better it sounded.

'Well done, Daniel!' said Mrs Morgan when he'd finished. 'I had no idea you were hiding all this talent.' She sounded really pleased.

Danny went off in a daze to clear up the broken glass.

As he was sweeping up what was left of the potion bottle, Laura Mills' name was called. Danny was surprised to see how nervous she looked. He gave her his best smile as she passed him.

'Go on,' he whispered. 'It's easy once you get started.'

The truth

A few days later, Danny stopped outside Uncle Hal's garage. He banged three times on the door. It lifted up and a hand pulled him inside.

'Danny! You're just in time!'

'I can't see, Uncle Hal. Turn the light on.'

But Uncle Hal took off Danny's glasses and replaced them with another pair. There was a click and two small beams of light lit up the room.

'The Light Specs! You finished them!' said Danny.

'That's right. They just needed a little fine tuning,' said Uncle Hal proudly.

'You're a genius, Uncle Hal. That Personality Potion was amazing.'

Uncle Hal looked blank for a moment. Then his face lit up.

'You mean it worked? You got the part in the play?'

'You're looking at Bugsy Malone,' said Danny. 'You should have seen Mark Shaw's face when Mrs Morgan told everyone.'

And Danny went on to tell Uncle Hal the whole story of what had happened with Wicks and the audition. Laura had got a part as a singer so he'd be seeing her all the time.

'It was funny though,' he said finally, 'I did the audition without drinking the potion. I suppose I must have still been feeling the after-effects.'

He looked at Uncle Hal who was grinning like a cat that's got the cream.

'What? What's so funny?'

'Shall I show you what was in that Personality Potion?' said Uncle Hal. He went into the kitchen and came back with two bottles. Inside them was the green liquid and the white powder. He showed Danny the labels.

'Green food colouring and bicarbonate of soda. That gave it the fizz,' said Uncle Hal. 'Your aunt uses them to make cakes. That's all I put in the potion.'

Danny stared at the bottles in disbelief. 'You mean it was all a trick? There wasn't really a Personality Potion?'

Uncle Hal shook his head, still grinning.

'But how come it changed me?' asked Danny. 'I was a different person.'

'Because you believed in the potion. But really, you were just believing in yourself. There was no magic.'

'Wow!' said Danny. He didn't know whether to be cross or pleased.

He'd meant to ask Uncle Hal for more of the Personality Potion. But now it turned out that he didn't need it. From now on he'd just have to manage on his own.

'I suppose, when you think about it, I must be fairly normal really,' he said out loud.

'Normal? Who wants to be normal?' said Uncle Hal, putting on his purple Light Specs. 'I'd say anyone who's playing the lead part in the school play must be pretty special.'

About the author

I have been writing stories for radio, television and books for many years. I live in Nottingham and work in a top attic room where no one can disturb me.

I often try out my stories on my two children at bathtime. If they stop shouting and splashing me, I know it must be a good story.

This story was inspired by reading *Dr Jekyll and Mr Hyde*, by Robert Louis Stevenson. I started thinking what would happen if a boy had a potion which gave him 'extra' personality – rather than turning him into a monster.

Other Treetops books at this level include:

I Wish, I Wish by Paul Shipton
The Goalie's Secret by Paul Shipton
The Ultimate Trainers by Paul Shipton
Waiting for Goldie by Susan Gates
The Case of the Smiling Shark by Tessa Krailing

Also available in packs

Stage 13 pack B	0 19 916918 7
Stage 13 class pack B	0 19 916919 5